HITS OF THE YEAR

THE YEAR

GUITAR CHORD SONGBOOK

Published by
Wise Publications
14-15 Berners Street, London W1T 3LJ, UK.

Exclusive Distributors:
Music Sales Limited
Distribution Centre, Newmarket Road,
Bury St Edmunds, Suffolk IP33 3YB, UK.

Music Sales Pty Limited
Units 3-4, 17 Willfox Street, Condell Park, NSW 2200, Australia.

Order No. AM1010317
ISBN: 978-1-78305-884-6
This book © Copyright 2014 Wise Publications,
a division of Music Sales Limited.

Edited by Adrian Hopkins.
Music arranged by Matt Cowe.
Music processed by Paul Ewers Music Design.
Cover photos:
Taylor Swift - Larry Busacca/TAS/Getty Images for TAS –
Angus Young - Rob Verhorst/Getty Images –
Ed Sheeran - C Brandon/Redferns via Getty Images.

Printed in the EU.

Your Guarantee of Quality

As publishers, we strive to produce every book
to the highest commercial standards.

The music has been freshly engraved and the
book has been carefully designed to minimise
awkward page turns and to make playing from
it a real pleasure.

Particular care has been given to specifying acid-free,
neutral-sized paper made from pulps which have
not been elemental chlorine bleached. This pulp is
from farmed sustainable forests and was produced
with special regard for the environment.

Throughout, the printing and binding have been
planned to ensure a sturdy, attractive publication
which should give years of enjoyment.

If your copy fails to meet our high standards,
please inform us and we will gladly replace it.

www.musicsales.com

HITS OF THE YEAR

GUITAR CHORD SONGBOOK

WISE PUBLICATIONS
part of The Music Sales Group

London / New York / Paris / Sydney / Copenhagen / Berlin / Madrid / Hong Kong / Tokyo

Relative Tuning

The guitar can be tuned with the aid of pitch pipes or dedicated electronic guitar tuners which are available through your local music dealer. If you do not have a tuning device, you can use relative tuning. Estimate the pitch of the 6th string as near as possible to E or at least a comfortable pitch (not too high, as you might break other strings in tuning up). Then, while checking the various positions on the diagram, place a finger from your left hand on the:

5th fret of the E or 6th string and **tune the open A** (or 5th string) to the note (**A**)

5th fret of the A or 5th string and **tune the open D** (or 4th string) to the note (**D**)

5th fret of the D or 4th string and **tune the open G** (or 3rd string) to the note (**G**)

4th fret of the G or 3rd string and **tune the open B** (or 2nd string) to the note (**B**)

5th fret of the B or 2nd string and **tune the open E** (or 1st string) to the note (**E**)

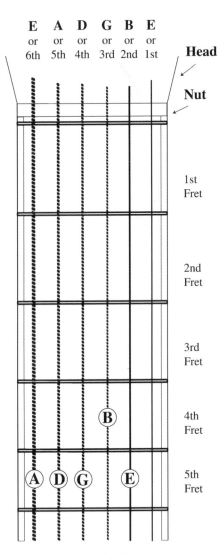

Reading Chord Boxes

Chord boxes are diagrams of the guitar neck viewed head upwards, face on as illustrated. The top horizontal line is the nut, unless a higher fret number is indicated, the others are the frets.

The vertical lines are the strings, starting from E (or 6th) on the left to E (or 1st) on the right.

The black dots indicate where to place your fingers.

Strings marked with an O are played open, not fretted. Strings marked with an X should not be played.

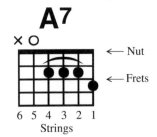

The curved bracket indicates a 'barre' - hold down the strings under the bracket with your first finger, using your other fingers to fret the remaining notes.

N.C. = No Chord.

All Of Me

Words and Music by John Stephens and Toby Gad

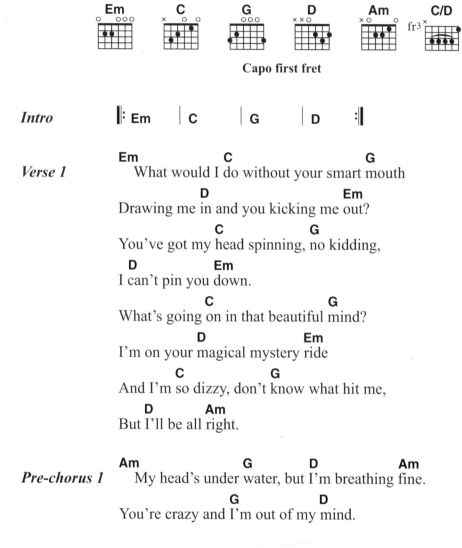

Capo first fret

Intro ‖: Em | C | G | D :‖

Verse 1

      Em   C   G
What would I do without your smart mouth
                 D   Em
Drawing me in and you kicking me out?
             C   G
You've got my head spinning, no kidding,
   D   Em
I can't pin you down.
             C   G
What's going on in that beautiful mind?
           D   Em
I'm on your magical mystery ride
           C   G
And I'm so dizzy, don't know what hit me,
   D   Am
But I'll be all right.

Pre-chorus 1

   Am   G   D   Am
My head's under water, but I'm breathing fine.
               G   D
You're crazy and I'm out of my mind.

7

Chorus 1

           G   Em
'Cause all of me loves all of you.

            C
Love your curves and all your edges,

        C/D   D
All your perfect imper - fections.

           G   Em
Give your all to me, I'll give my all to you.

           C
You're my end and my beginning,

       C/D   D
Even when I lose I'm winning.

                Em C   G   D
'Cause I give you all___ of me,

                Em C   G   D
And you give me all___ of you, oh.___

Verse 2

Em   C   G
  How many times do I have to tell you

                    D   Em
Even when you're crying you're beautiful too?

             C   G
The world is beating you down,

        D   Em
I'm a - round through every mood.

           C   G
You're my downfall, you're my muse,

           D   Em
My worst dis - traction, my rhythm and blues.

           C   G
I can't stop singing, it's ringing

      D   Am
In my head for you.

Pre-chorus 2   As Pre-chorus 1

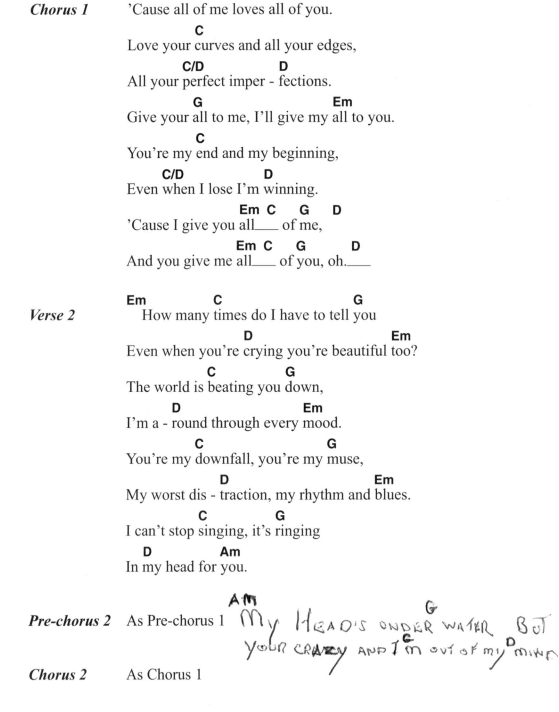

Chorus 2   As Chorus 1

Bridge

D   Am
Give me all of you,

          G   D   Am
Cards on the table, we're both showing hearts.

          G   D
Risking it all, though it's hard.

Chorus 3

          G   Em
'Cause all of me loves all of you.

          C
Love your curves and all your edges,

        C/D   D
All your perfect imper - fections.

          G   Em
Give your all to me, I'll give my all to you.

          C
You're my end and my beginning,

        C/D   D
Even when I lose I'm winning.

              Em C   G   D
'Cause I give you all___ of me,

              Em C   G   D
And you give me all___ of you.

         Em C   G   D
I give you all___ of me,

         Em C   G   D
And you give me all___ of you, oh.___

D   Am
I am Breathing Fine

A Sky Full Of Stars

Words & Music by Guy Berryman, Jonathan Buckland,
William Champion, Christopher Martin & Tim Bergling

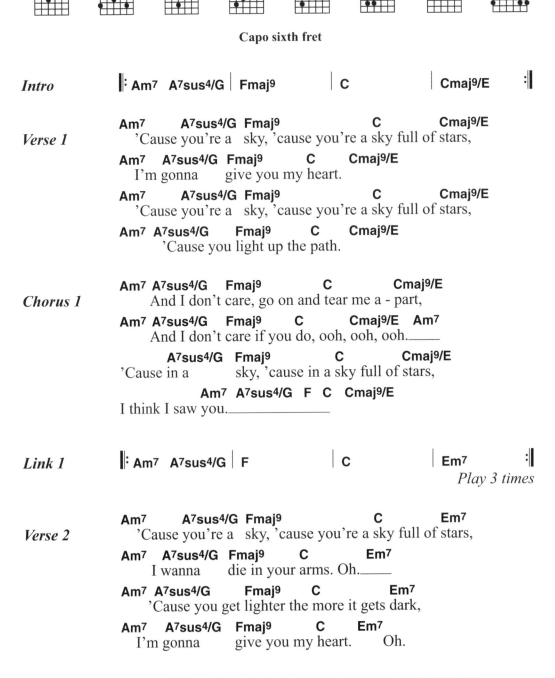

Capo sixth fret

Intro

$\|$: Am⁷ A⁷sus⁴/G | Fmaj⁹ | C | Cmaj⁹/E :$\|$

Verse 1

Am⁷   A⁷sus⁴/G Fmaj⁹   C   Cmaj⁹/E
'Cause you're a   sky, 'cause you're a sky full of stars,

Am⁷   A⁷sus⁴/G Fmaj⁹   C   Cmaj⁹/E
I'm gonna   give you my heart.

Am⁷   A⁷sus⁴/G Fmaj⁹   C   Cmaj⁹/E
'Cause you're a   sky, 'cause you're a sky full of stars,

Am⁷ A⁷sus⁴/G   Fmaj⁹   C   Cmaj⁹/E
'Cause you light up the path.

Chorus 1

Am⁷ A⁷sus⁴/G   Fmaj⁹   C   Cmaj⁹/E
And I don't care, go on and tear me a - part,

Am⁷ A⁷sus⁴/G   Fmaj⁹   C   Cmaj⁹/E Am⁷
And I don't care if you do, ooh, ooh, ooh.____

A⁷sus⁴/G Fmaj⁹   C   Cmaj⁹/E
'Cause in a   sky, 'cause in a sky full of stars,

Am⁷ A⁷sus⁴/G F C Cmaj⁹/E
I think I saw you._____

Link 1

$\|$: Am⁷ A⁷sus⁴/G | F | C | Em⁷ :$\|$

Play 3 times

Verse 2

Am⁷   A⁷sus⁴/G Fmaj⁹   C   Em⁷
'Cause you're a   sky, 'cause you're a sky full of stars,

Am⁷   A⁷sus⁴/G Fmaj⁹   C   Em⁷
I wanna   die in your arms. Oh.____

Am⁷ A⁷sus⁴/G   Fmaj⁹   C   Em⁷
'Cause you get lighter the more it gets dark,

Am⁷ A⁷sus⁴/G   Fmaj⁹   C   Em⁷
I'm gonna   give you my heart.   Oh.

Chorus 2

Am7 A7sus4   F   C   Em7
And I don't care, go on and tear me a - part,

Am7 A7sus4   F   C   Em7   Am7
And I don't care if you do, ooh, ooh, ooh._____

        A7sus4/G   Fmaj9   C   Em7
'Cause in a   sky, 'cause in a sky full of stars,

           Am7 A7sus4/G F C Em7
I think I see you._____

           Am7 A7sus4/G F C (Em7)
I think I see you._____

Link 2

𝄆 Am7 A7sus4/G | F | C | Em7   𝄇

Play 4 times

Instrumental

𝄆 Fmaj9 | G | Am7 | Am7 C   𝄇

Bridge

Fmaj9   C   Am7
  'Cause you're a sky, you're a sky full of stars,

    C   Fmaj9 G Am7
Such a heavenly view._____

           C   Fmaj9 G Am7
You're such a heavenly view._____

             C
Yeah, yeah, yeah,____ whoo.

Outro

| Fmaj9 | G | Am7 | Am7 C |

𝄆 Fmaj9 | G | Am7 | Am7 C   𝄇
                                                Ooh.

All About That Bass

Words & Music by Kevin Kadish & Meghan Trainor

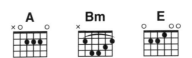

Intro

    N.C.   A
Because you know I'm all about that bass, 'bout that bass, no treble.

    Bm
I'm all about that bass, 'bout that bass, no treble.

    E
I'm all about that bass, 'bout that bass, no treble.

    A
I'm all about that bass, 'bout that bass, bass, bass, bass, bass.

Verse 1

  A
    Yeah, it's pretty clear: I ain't no size two.

Bm
    But I can shake it, shake it like I'm supposed to do.

  E
    'Cause I got that boom-boom that all the boys chase,

      A
And all the right junk in all the right places.

Verse 2

  A
    I see the magazine working that Photoshop.

Bm
    We know that shit ain't real, come on now, make it stop.

  E
    If you got beauty, beauty, just raise 'em up,

       A
'Cause every inch of you is perfect, from the bottom to the top.

Pre-chorus 1

                       A
Yeah, my mama she told me don't worry about your size.

Bm
    (wop, wop, cha-ooh, wop, wop)

             E
She says, "Boys like a little more booty to hold at night."

A
    (da booty, booty, da, da booty)

You know I won't be no stick figure silicone Barbie doll.

Bm
    (wop, wop, cha-ooh, wop, wop)

      E   A
So if that's what you're into then go ahead and move a - long.

Chorus 1

N.C   A
Because you know I'm all about that bass, 'bout that bass, no treble.

     Bm
I'm all about that bass, 'bout that bass, no treble.

     E
I'm all about that bass, 'bout that bass, no treble.

     A
I'm all about that bass, 'bout that bass, hey!

Verse 3

               A   Bm
I'm bringing booty back. Go ahead and tell them skinny bitches that.

                          E
No, I'm just playing! I know   you think you're fat.

But I'm here to tell you:

    A
Every inch of you is perfect, from the bottom to the top.

Pre-chorus 2   As Pre-chorus 1

Chorus 2   As Chorus 1

Chorus 3   As Chorus 1

Chorus 4   As Chorus 1

Outro | A | A | Bm | Bm | E | E | A | A (N.C.) ‖

Budapest

Words & Music by George Ezra Barnett & Joel Laslett Pott

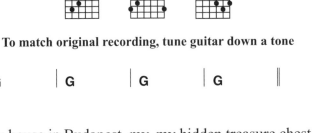

To match original recording, tune guitar down a tone

Intro | G | G | G | G   ‖

Verse 1
G
My house in Budapest, my, my hidden treasure chest,

Golden grand piano, my beautiful Castillo.
C   G
You, ooh, you, ooh, I'd leave it all.

My acres of a land, I have achieved.

It may be hard for you to stop and believe.
C   G
But for you, ooh, you, ooh, I'd leave it all.
C   G
Oh for you, ooh, you, ooh, I'd leave it all.

Chorus 1
D   C   G
Give me one good reason why I should never make a change.
D   C   G
And baby if you hold me then all of this will go a - way.

Verse 2
G
My many artifacts, the list goes on,

If you just say the words, I'll, I'll up and run.
C   G
Oh, to you, ooh, you, ooh, I'd leave it all.
C   G
Oh, to you, ooh, you, ooh, I'd leave it all.

Chorus 2   As Chorus 1

Chorus 3   As Chorus 1

Instrumental | G | G | G | G |

             | C | C | G | G   ‖

                 G
Verse 3   My friends and family, they, don't understand,

             They fear they'd lose so much if you take my hand.
                     C   G
             But, for you, ooh, you, ooh, I'd lose it all.
                     C   G
             Oh for you, ooh, you, ooh, I'd lose it all.

Chorus 4   As Chorus 1

Chorus 5   As Chorus 1

                 G
Verse 4   My house in Budapest, my, my hidden treasure chest,

             Golden grand piano, my beautiful Castillo.
             C   G
             You, ooh, you, ooh, I'd leave it all.
                     C   G
             Oh for you, ooh, you, ooh I'd leave it all.

Counting Stars

Words & Music by Ryan Tedder

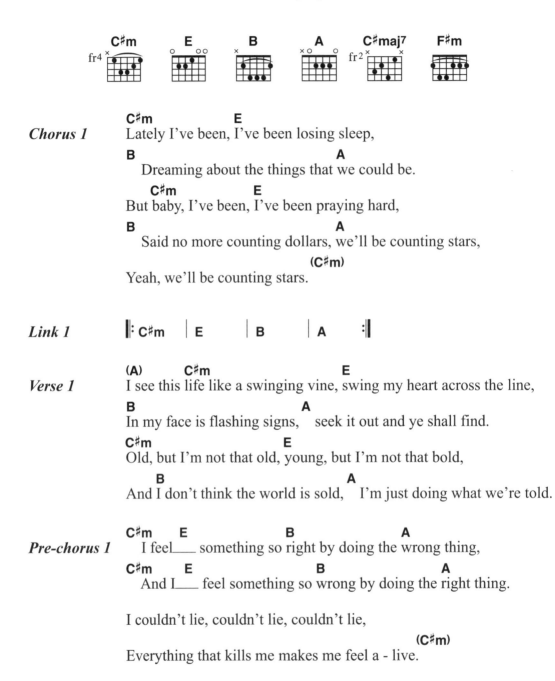

Chorus 1

     C#m   E
Lately I've been, I've been losing sleep,

B   A
   Dreaming about the things that we could be.

     C#m   E
But baby, I've been, I've been praying hard,

B   A
   Said no more counting dollars, we'll be counting stars,

                  (C#m)
Yeah, we'll be counting stars.

Link 1

‖: C#m | E | B | A   :‖

Verse 1

(A)   C#m   E
I see this life like a swinging vine, swing my heart across the line,

B   A
In my face is flashing signs,   seek it out and ye shall find.

C#m   E
Old, but I'm not that old, young, but I'm not that bold,

      B   A
And I don't think the world is sold,   I'm just doing what we're told.

Pre-chorus 1

C#m   E   B   A
  I feel___ something so right by doing the wrong thing,

C#m   E   B   A
  And I___ feel something so wrong by doing the right thing.

I couldn't lie, couldn't lie, couldn't lie,

                         (C#m)
Everything that kills me makes me feel a - live.

Chorus 2

C♯m   E
Lately I've been, I've been losing sleep,
B   A
Dreaming about the things that we could be.
      C♯m   E
But baby, I've been, I've been praying hard,
B   A   (C♯m)
  Said no more counting dollars, we'll be counting stars.
C♯m   E
Lately I've been, I've been losing sleep,
B   A
Dreaming about the things that we could be.
      C♯m   E
But baby, I've been, I've been praying hard,
B   A   (C♯m)
  Said no more counting dollars, we'll be, we'll be counting stars.

Link 2 | C♯m | E | B | A   ‖

Verse 2

(A)   C♯m   E
I feel the love and I feel it burn down this river every turn,
B   A   N.C.
Hope is our four letter word, make that money, watch it burn.
C♯m   E
Old, but I'm not that old, young, but I'm not that bold,
     B   A
And I don't think the world is sold,   I'm just doing what we're told.

Pre-chorus 2

C♯m   E   B   A
And I__ feel something so wrong by doing the right thing.

I couldn't lie, couldn't lie, couldn't lie,
                                    (C♯m)
Everything that drowns me makes me wanna fly.

Chorus 3   As Chorus 2

Bridge

C♯maj7 (N.C.)
Oh, take that money watch it burn,

Sink in the river, the lessons I learned.

Take that money watch it burn,

Sink in the river, the lessons I learned.

Take that money watch it burn,

Sink in the river, the lessons I learned
(C♯m)
Take that money watch it burn,

Sink in the river, the lessons I learned
A   F♯m   (C♯m)
Everything that kills me makes me feel a - live.

Chorus 4   As Chorus 2

Outro
C♯m
Take that money watch it burn,
E
Sink in the river, the lessons I learned.
B
Take that money watch it burn,
A
Sink in the river, the lessons I learned.
C♯m
Take that money watch it burn,
E
Sink in the river, the lessons I learned.
B
Take that money watch it burn,
(A)
Sink in the river, the lessons I learned.

Ghost

Words & Music by Ryan Tedder, Noel Zancanella & Ella Henderson

Chorus 1

D A F♯m E
I keep going to the river to pray,

D   A F♯m   E
'Cause I need something that can wash all the pain.

D   A   F♯m   E
And at most I'm sleeping all these demons away,

D   A   F♯m   E   N.C.
But your ghost, the ghost of you, well, it keeps me a - wake.

Verse 1

N.C.   F♯m
My friends had you figured out, yeah, they saw what's inside of you.

             D   Bm7
You tried hiding an - other you, but your evil was coming through.

          F♯m
These guys sitting on the wall, they watch every move I make.

          D   Bm7
Bright light living in the shade, your cold heart makes my spirit shake.

Pre-chorus 1

A   Bm7   F♯m
 I had to go through hell to prove I'm not insane,

   D
Had to meet the devil just to know his name.

       E
And that's when my love was burning,

Yeah, it's still burning.

Chorus 2

D A F♯m E
I keep going to the river to pray,

D A F♯m E
'Cause I need something that can wash all the pain.

D A F♯m E
And at most I'm sleeping all these demons away,

D A F♯m E
But your ghost, the ghost of you, well, it keeps me awake.

D A F♯m E
I keep going to the river to pray,

D A F♯m E
'Cause I need something that can wash all the pain.

D A F♯m E
And at most I'm sleeping all these demons away,

D A F♯m N.C.
But your ghost, the ghost of you, well, it keeps me awake.

Verse 2

N.C. F♯m
Each time that I think you go, I turn around and you're creeping in.

D Bm7
And I let you un - der my skin, 'cause I love living in the sin.

F♯m
Boy, you never told me true love was going to hurt.

D Bm7
True pain I don't deserve, truth is that I never learn.

Chorus 3   As Chorus 2

Bridge

D A
Give up the ghost,   give up the ghost,

F♯m E
Give up the ghost,___ stop the haunting baby.

D A
Give up the ghost,   give up the ghost,

F♯m E
Give up the ghost,___ no more haunting baby.

N.C.
I keep going to the river.

Chorus 4

          D A   F♯m   E
          I keep going to the river to pray,

          D   A   F♯m   E
          'Cause I need something that can wash all the pain.

          D   A   F♯m   E
          And at most I'm sleeping all these demons away,

          D   A   F♯m   E
          But your ghost, the ghost of you, well, it keeps me awake.

          D A   F♯m   E
          I keep going to the river to pray,

          D   A   F♯m   E
          'Cause I need something that can wash all the pain.

          N.C.
          And at most I'm sleeping all these demons away,

          But your ghost, the ghost of you, well, it keeps me awake.

God Only Knows

Words & Music by Brian Wilson & Tony Asher

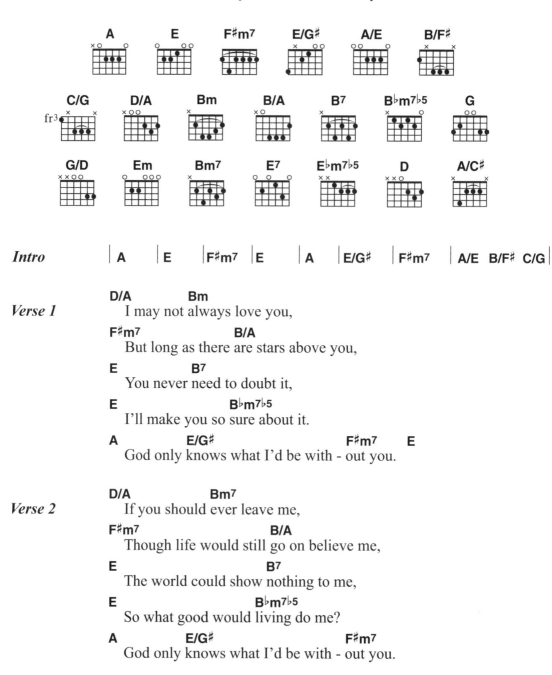

Intro | A | E |F♯m7 | E | A |E/G♯ |F♯m7 |A/E B/F♯ C/G |

Verse 1

D/A   Bm
I may not always love you,

F♯m7   B/A
But long as there are stars above you,

E   B7
You never need to doubt it,

E   B♭m7♭5
I'll make you so sure about it.

A   E/G♯   F♯m7 E
God only knows what I'd be with - out you.

Verse 2

D/A   Bm7
If you should ever leave me,

F♯m7   B/A
Though life would still go on believe me,

E   B7
The world could show nothing to me,

E   B♭m7♭5
So what good would living do me?

A   E/G♯   F♯m7
God only knows what I'd be with - out you.

Instrumental | A/E | G | A/E | G |

                 | G/D | Em | Bm⁷ | E |

                 | A | E⁷ | A | E♭m⁷♭5 |

D   A/C♯   Bm⁷
God only knows what I'd be with - out you.

D/A   Bm⁷
Verse 3   If you should ever leave me,
F♯m⁷   B/A
    Though life would still go on believe me.
E   B⁷
    The world could show nothing to me,
E   B♭m⁷♭5
    So what good would living do me?
A   E/G♯   F♯m   E/G♯
God only knows what I'd be with - out you.

             A   E/G♯   F♯m   E/G♯
Outro   ‖: God only knows what I'd be with - out you,

(God only knows what I'd be without you)
A   E/G♯   F♯m   E/G♯
God only knows what I'd be with - out you,

(God only knows what I'd be without you)   :‖ *Repeat to fade*

23

Happy

Words & Music by Pharrell Williams

F7   B♭   C   D♭maj7   Cm7   Csus4

Verse 1

F7 N.C.   F7 B♭ C B♭
It might seem crazy what I'm about to say,

F7 N.C.   F7 B♭ C B♭
Sunshine she's here, you can take a break.

F7 N.C.   F7 B♭ C
I'm a   hot air balloon that could go to space,

B♭   F7 N.C.   F7 B♭ C
With the air,   like I don't care baby, by the way.

Chorus 1

B♭   D♭maj7
Be - cause I'm happy.

        Cm7   Csus4   F7
Clap along if you feel like a room without a roof.

        D♭maj7
Because I'm happy.

        Cm7   Csus4   F7
Clap along if you feel like happiness is the truth.

        D♭maj7
Because I'm happy.

        Cm7   Csus4   F7
Clap along if you know what happiness is to you.

        D♭maj7
Because I'm happy.

        Cm7   Csus4   F7
Clap along if you feel like that's what you wanna do.

Verse 2

F⁷ N.C.   F⁷ B♭ C B♭
Here come bad news talking this and that,   (Yeah)

F⁷ N.C.   F⁷ B♭ C B♭
Well, give me all you got, and don't hold it back.   (Yeah)

F⁷ N.C.   F⁷ B♭ C B♭
Well, I should probably warn you I'll be just fine,   (Yeah)

F⁷ N.C.   F⁷ B♭   C
No offense to you, don't waste your time,   here's why.

Verse 2

F⁷ N.C.
Here come bad news talking this and that, (Yeah)   [F⁷ B♭ C B♭]

F⁷ N.C.
Well, give me all you got, and don't hold it back. (Yeah)   [F⁷ B♭ C B♭]

F⁷ N.C.
Well, I should probably warn you I'll be just fine, (Yeah)   [F⁷ B♭ C B♭]

F⁷ N.C.
No offense to you, don't waste your time, here's why.   [F⁷ B♭ C]

Chorus 2   As Chorus 1

Bridge

F⁷ (N.C.)
Hey, come on, uh.

Bring me down, can't nothing bring me down.

My level's too high to bring me down,

Can't nothing bring me down.

I said, (let me tell you now, uh)

Bring me down, can't nothing bring me down.

My level's too high to bring me down.

Can't nothing bring me down, I said.

Chorus 3

(F⁷)   D♭maj⁷
Because I'm happy.
         Cm⁷   Csus⁴   F⁷
Clap along if you feel like a room without a roof.
         D♭maj⁷
Because I'm happy.
         Cm⁷   Csus⁴   F⁷
Clap along if you feel like happiness is the truth.
         D♭maj⁷
Because I'm happy.
         Cm⁷   Csus⁴   F⁷
Clap along if you know what happiness is to you.
         D♭maj⁷
Because I'm happy.
         Cm⁷   Csus⁴   F⁷
Clap along if you feel like that's what you wanna do.

Chorus 4   As Chorus 3

F7

Bridge 2   Hey, come on, uh.

Bring me down, can't nothing bring me down.

My level's too high to bring me down.

Can't nothing bring me down, I said.

Chorus 5   As Chorus 3

Chorus 6   As Chorus 3

Heart And Soul

Words & Music by Garret Lee, Sam McTrusty,
Ross McNae, Craig Kneale & Barry McKenna

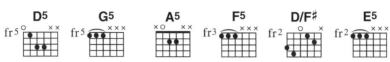

⑥ = D ③ = G
⑤ = A ② = B
④ = D ① = E

Intro | D5 | D5 | D5 | G5 A5 |

Verse 1

D5 N.C.
I flick the switch on the generator,

D5 N.C.
So I can turn you on.

D5 N.C.
You better get to know your operator,

G5   **A5**
Before you pick that tone.

D5 N.C.
You own the lock and the key,

D5 N.C.
For the window to my soul.

D5 N.C.
Yeah, that's the only thing you talk about,

G5   **A5**
You gotta let me know.

F5   **A5**   **D5**
Pre-chorus 1 'Cause it must have been something out of control.

                                    F5
Yeah, it must have been worth it

                                    G5
'Cause I had nothing left to show,

                        A5
How you put my life in your hands.

Chorus 1

         D5   **G5**   **A5** **G5** **A5**
When you open up your heart and your soul,

D5   **G5**   **A5** **G5** **D/F♯**
Take my love and never grow old, yeah.

D5   **G5**   **A5**
Open up your heart and your soul,

G5   **A5**   **D5**   **A5**
 'Cause if you're looking for something to love,

          G5   **D/F♯** **E5**
You've gotta let me know.

Verse 2

D5 N.C.
 I put the sun in an elevator

D5 N.C.
 And took it to my home.

D5 N.C.
 I'm still living on a ladder

        G5   **A5**
From the sky to the floor.

D5 N.C.
 Don't look down,

D5 N.C.
 You got a long way to go.

D5 N.C.
 And if you wanna live,

        G5   **A5**
You better let the mind go.

Pre-chorus 2   As Pre-chorus 1

Chorus 2   As Chorus 1

Instrumental | **D5** | **D5** | **D5** | **F5** |

               | **D5** | **D5** | **D5** | **G5** **A5** ‖

Verse 3

D5
    I flick the switch on the generator,

So I could turn you on.

Yeah, that's the only thing you talk about,
G5   **A5**   **D5**
    You gotta let me know.___
G5   **A5**
    You gotta let me know.

Chorus 3

D5   **G5**   **A5** **G5** **A5**
Open up your heart and your soul,
D5   **G5**   **A5**   **G5** **D/F♯**
Take my love and never grow old, yeah.
D5   **G5**   **A5**
Open up your heart and your soul,
G5   **A5**   **D5**
    'Cause if you're looking for something to love,
A5   **G5**   **D/F♯** **E5**
    You've gotta let me know._____

Chorus 4

D5   **G5**   **A5** **G5** **A5**
Open up your heart and your soul,
D5   **G5**   **A5**   **G5** **D/F♯**
Take my love and never grow old, yeah.
D5   **G5**   **A5**
Open up your heart and your soul,
G5   **A5**   **D5**
    'Cause if you're looking for something to love,
A5   **G5**   **D/F♯** **E5** **D5**
    You've gotta let me know._____

How Long Will I Love You

Words & Music by Mike Scott

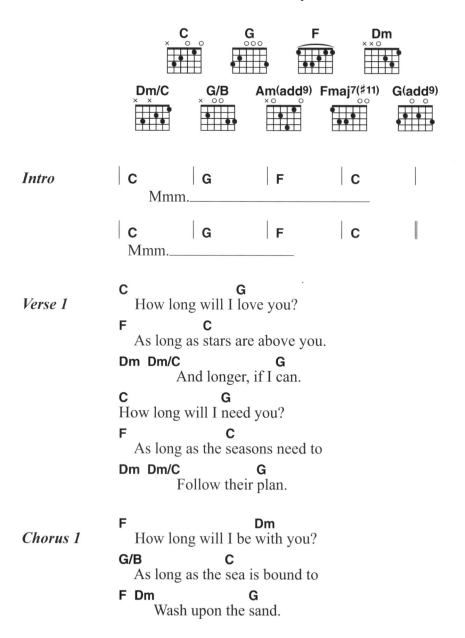

C   G   F   Dm

Dm/C   G/B   Am(add⁹) Fmaj7(♯11) G(add⁹)

Intro

| C | G | F | C |

Mmm._____

| C | G | F | C |

Mmm._____

Verse 1

```
C                    G
   How long will I love you?
F          C
   As long as stars are above you.
Dm Dm/C            G
        And longer, if I can.
C              G
How long will I need you?
F               C
   As long as the seasons need to
Dm Dm/C          G
        Follow their plan.
```

Chorus 1

```
F                Dm
   How long will I be with you?
G/B           C
   As long as the sea is bound to
F Dm           G
   Wash upon the sand.
```

Verse 2

C   G
How long will I want you?

F   C
As long as you want me to

Dm Dm/C   G
And longer by far.

C   G
How long will I hold you?

F   C
As long as your father told you,

Dm   Dm/C   G
As long as you can.

Chorus 2

F   Dm
How long will I give to you?

G/B   C
As long as I live through you

F Dm   G
However long you say.

Verse 3

C   G
How long will I love you?

F   C
As long as stars are above you

Dm Dm/C   G
And longer, if I may.

Instrumental | C | G | F | C |
Mmm._____

| Dm | Dm/C | G | G   ‖
Mmm._____

Outro

C   G/B
How long will I love you?

Am(add9)   G   Fmaj7(#11) G(add9) C
As long as stars are above you.

I See Fire

Words & Music by Ed Sheeran

Am   Fmaj⁷   G   C   Dsus²   Dm

To match original recording, tune guitar up one semitone

Intro

N.C.
Oh, misty eye of the mountain below,

Keep careful watch of my brothers' souls.

And should the sky be filled with fire and smoke,
                          Am
Keep watching over Durin's sons.

Link 1 | Am Fmaj⁷ | G Am | Am Fmaj⁷ | G Am   ‖

Verse 1

Am   **C**   **G**   **Fmaj⁷**
If this is to end in fire, then we should all burn to - gether,
            Am   **C** **G**   **Dsus²**
Watch the flames climb high into the night.
            Am   **C** **G**   **Fmaj⁷**
Calling out father,   oh, stand by and we will
            Dm   **C**   **Fmaj⁷**
Watch the flames burn auburn on the mountain side high.

Link 2 | Am Fmaj⁷ | G Am   ‖

Verse 2

Am　　　　　　　　　　　　C　　　　　　　　　　G　　　　Fmaj7
And if we should die to - night, then we should all die to - gether,

　　　　　　　　Am　　C　　G　　　Dsus2
Raise a glass of wine for the last time.

　　　　　　　　　Am　　　　C　　G　　　　Fmaj7
Calling out father,　　oh, prepare as we will

　　　　　　　　　Dm　　　　　　C　　　　　　Fmaj7
Watch the flames burn auburn on the mountain side,

　　　　　　　Dm　　C　　　　　　　　　Fmaj7
Deso - lation comes upon the sky.

Chorus 1

(Fmaj7)　　　Am　Fmaj7　G　　　　　Am
Now, I see fire　　　　　inside the mountain,

　　　　　　　Fmaj7　G　　　　　Am
I see fire　　　　　burning the trees.

　　　　　　　　　　Fmaj7　G　　　　Am
And I see fire＿＿＿＿＿ hollowing souls,

　　　　　　　Fmaj7　G　　　　　　Dsus2
I see fire,＿＿＿＿＿ blood in the breeze.

And I hope that you remember me.

Link 3

| Am　Fmaj7 | G　Am　　　 | Am　Fmaj7 | G　Am　　　 ‖

Verse 3

Am　　　　　　　　　　　　C　　　　　　　　G　　　　Fmaj7
Oh, should my people fall, then surely I'll do the same,

　　　　　　　　　Am　　　C　　　　　　G　　　　Dsus2
Confined in mountain halls, we got too close to the flame.

　　　　　　　　　Am　　　C　　G　　　　Fmaj7
Calling out father,　　oh, hold fast and we will

　　　　　　　　　Dm　　　　　　C　　　　　　Fmaj7
Watch the flames burn auburn on the mountain side,

　　　　　　　Dm　　C　　　　　　　　　Fmaj7
Deso - lation comes upon the sky.

Chorus 2　　　　As Chorus 1

Bridge

Dsus²   Dm   Am   C   G
And if the night is burning, I will cover my eyes,

         Dm   Am   C   G
For if the dark re - turns, then my brothers will die.

         Dm   Am   C   G
And as the sky is falling down it crashed in - to this lonely town,

           Dm
And with that shadow upon the ground

   C   Fmaj⁷   G
I hear my people screaming out.___

Chorus 3

(G)   Am   Fmaj⁷   G   Am
Now, I see fire   inside the mountain,

        Fmaj⁷   G   Am
I see fire   burning the trees.

           Fmaj⁷   G   Am
And I see fire___ hollowing souls,

        Fmaj⁷   G   Am
I see fire,___ blood in the breeze.

Outro

Am   Fmaj⁷   G   Am
I see fire, oh   you know I saw a city burning.

           Fmaj⁷   G   Am
And I see fire, feel the heat upon my skin, yeah.

          Fmaj⁷   G   Am
And I see fire, ooh.___

           Fmaj⁷   G   Am
And I see fire burn auburn on the mountain side.

Love Never Felt So Good

Words & Music by Michael Jackson & Paul Anka

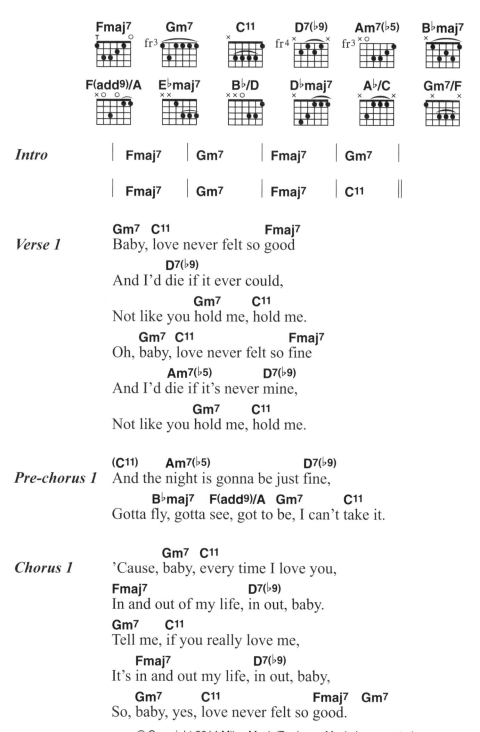

Intro

| Fmaj7 | Gm7 | Fmaj7 | Gm7 |

| Fmaj7 | Gm7 | Fmaj7 | C11 |

Verse 1

   Gm7 C11   Fmaj7
Baby, love never felt so good
       D7(♭9)
And I'd die if it ever could,
          Gm7   C11
Not like you hold me, hold me.
    Gm7 C11   Fmaj7
Oh, baby, love never felt so fine
      Am7(♭5)   D7(♭9)
And I'd die if it's never mine,
         Gm7   C11
Not like you hold me, hold me.

Pre-chorus 1

  (C11)   Am7(♭5)   D7(♭9)
And the night is gonna be just fine,
       B♭maj7 F(add9)/A Gm7   C11
Gotta fly, gotta see, got to be, I can't take it.

Chorus 1

       Gm7 C11
'Cause, baby, every time I love you,
Fmaj7   D7(♭9)
In and out of my life, in out, baby.
Gm7   C11
Tell me, if you really love me,
     Fmaj7   D7(♭9)
It's in and out my life, in out, baby,
     Gm7   C11   Fmaj7 Gm7
So, baby, yes, love never felt so good.

Verse 2

Gm⁷   C¹¹   Fmaj⁷
Baby, love never felt so fine
       D7(♭9)
And I'd die if it ever mine,
         Gm⁷   C¹¹
Not like you hold me, hold me.
      Gm⁷   C¹¹   Fmaj⁷
Oh, baby, love never felt so good
        Am7(♭5)   D7(♭9)
And I'd die if it ever could,
         Gm⁷   C¹¹
Not like you hold me, hold me.

Pre-chorus 2

(C¹¹)   Am7(♭5)   D7(♭9)
And the night is gonna be just fine,
       B♭maj⁷   F(add9)/A   Gm⁷   C¹¹
Gotta fly, gotta see, can't be - lieve, I can't take it.

Chorus 2

       Gm⁷   C¹¹
'Cause baby, every time I love you,
     Fmaj⁷   D7(♭9)
It's in and out my life, in out, baby.
Gm⁷   C¹¹
Tell me, if you really love me,
     Fmaj⁷   D7(♭9)
It's in and out my life driving me crazy,
Gm⁷   C¹¹
Baby, love never felt so good.

Interlude | E♭maj⁷ | B♭/D | D♭maj⁷ | A♭/C |

                      | Am7(♭5)   D7(♭9) | Gm⁷   Gm7/F | E♭maj⁷   B♭maj⁷ | C¹¹   ‖

Verse 3   As Verse 2

Pre-chorus 3   As Pre-chorus 2

Chorus 3   As Chorus 2

Outro

Fmaj7   **C11**
   Never felt so good (oh yeah)

Never felt so good,
Fmaj7   **C11**
   Never felt so good,

Never felt so good,
Fmaj7   **C11**
   Never felt so good (yeah, yeah)
               Fmaj7   **Gm7**
Never felt so good   (uh huh)
             Fmaj7
Never felt so good.

Let It Go

Words & Music by Kirsten Anderson-Lopez and Robert Lopez

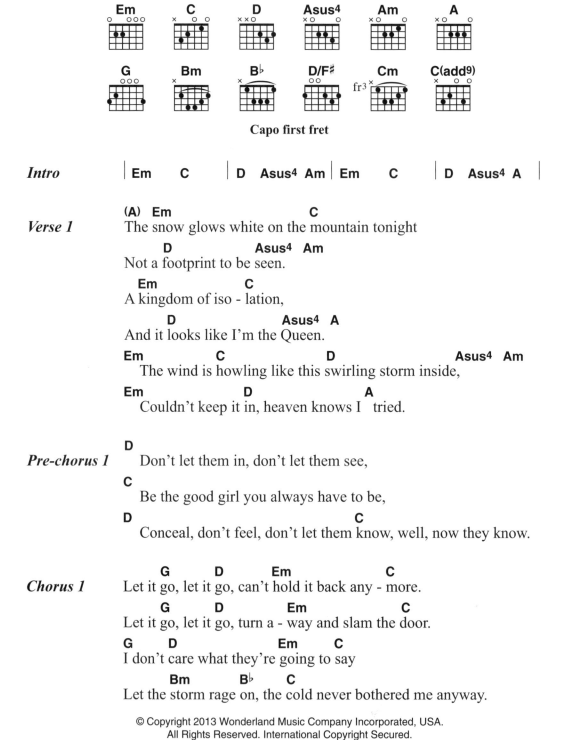

Capo first fret

Intro | Em   C | D Asus4 Am | Em   C | D Asus4 A |

Verse 1

(A) Em   **C**
The snow glows white on the mountain tonight
        D   **Asus4 Am**
Not a footprint to be seen.
      Em   **C**
A kingdom of iso - lation,
          D   **Asus4 A**
And it looks like I'm the Queen.
Em   **C**   **D**   **Asus4 Am**
    The wind is howling like this swirling storm inside,
Em   **D**   **A**
    Couldn't keep it in, heaven knows I   tried.

Pre-chorus 1

      D
      Don't let them in, don't let them see,
      C
      Be the good girl you always have to be,
D   **C**
      Conceal, don't feel, don't let them know, well, now they know.

Chorus 1

        G   **D**   **Em**   **C**
Let it go, let it go, can't hold it back any - more.
        G   **D**   **Em**   **C**
Let it go, let it go, turn a - way and slam the door.
G   **D**   **Em**   **C**
I don't care what they're going to say
        Bm   **B♭**   **C**
Let the storm rage on, the cold never bothered me anyway.

Link | **G**   **D/F♯** |

Verse 2
    Em   **C**
    It's funny how some distance
         D   **Am**
    Makes everything seem small.
           Em   **D**
    And the fears that once con - trolled me
           Asus⁴   **A**
    Can't get to me at all.

Pre-chorus 2
    D
    It's time to see what I can do,
    C
    To test the limits and break through,
    D   **C**
    No right, no wrong, no rules for me, I'm free.

Chorus 2
        G   **D**   **Em**   **C**
    Let it go, let it go, I am one with the wind and sky.
        G   **D**   **Em**   **C**
    Let it go, let it go, you'll never see me cry.
    G   **D**   **Em**   **C**
    Here I stand and here I'll stay,
        Bm   **B♭**   **(C)**
    Let the storm rage on.

Bridge
    C
    My power flurries through the air into the ground,

    My soul is spiraling in frozen fractals all around.
    D
    And one thought crystallizes like an icy blast,
    Em   **C**   **D**   **Am**   **C**
    I'm never going back, the past is in the past.___

Outro chorus
    N.C. G   **D**   **Em**   **C**
    Let it go, let it go, and I'll rise like the break of dawn.
        G   **D**   **Em**   **C**
    Let it go, let it go, that perfect girl is gone.
    G   **D**   **Em**   **C** **Cm**   **Bm**   **B♭**
    Here I stand in the light of day,___ let the storm rage on,
        C(add⁹)
    The cold never bothered me anyway.

Magic

Words & Music by Guy Berryman, Jonathan Buckland,
William Champion & Christopher Martin

D   A   E   A/C♯   C♯m7   Dsus2

Intro   ‖: D | D A | E | E A/C♯ :‖

Verse 1

(A/C♯) D   A   E
Call it magic, call it true,

A/C♯ D   A   E
Call it magic when I'm with you.

    A/C♯   D   A   E
And I just got broken, broken into two,

        A/C♯ D   A   E
Still I call it magic when I'm next to you.

Chorus 1

A/C♯   D
    And I don't, and I don't and I don't, and I don't,

    A
No, I don't, it's true,

    E
I don't, no, I don't, no, I don't, no,

                A/C♯
I don't want anybody else but you.

    D
I don't, no, I don't, no, I don't, no, I don't,

    A
No, I don't, it's true,

    E
I don't, no, I don't, no, I don't, no,

                A/C♯
I don't want anybody else but you.

Link 1 | D | D A | E | E A/C♯ ‖

Ooh, ooh, ooh.

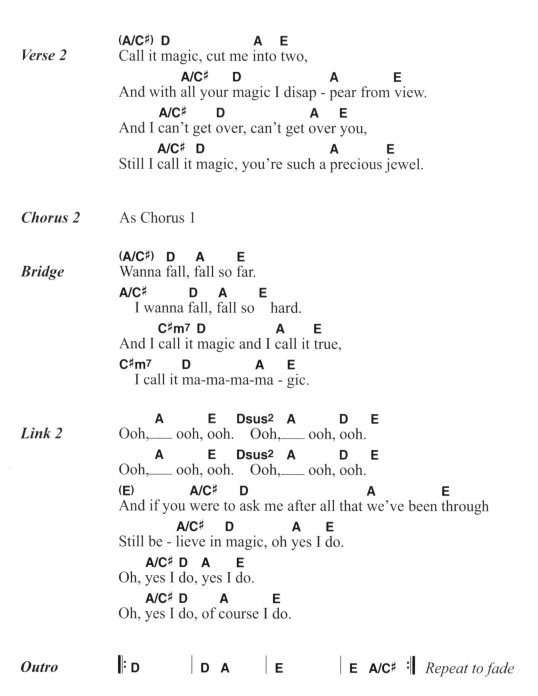

Verse 2

(A/C#) D   A E
Call it magic, cut me into two,

     A/C#   D   A   E
And with all your magic I disap - pear from view.

     A/C#   D   A   E
And I can't get over, can't get over you,

     A/C# D   A   E
Still I call it magic, you're such a precious jewel.

Chorus 2   As Chorus 1

Bridge

(A/C#) D A   E
Wanna fall, fall so far.

A/C#   D A   E
  I wanna fall, fall so   hard.

      C#m7 D   A   E
And I call it magic and I call it true,

C#m7   D   A   E
  I call it ma-ma-ma-ma - gic.

Link 2

      A   E Dsus2 A   D E
Ooh,___ ooh, ooh.   Ooh,___ ooh, ooh.

      A   E Dsus2 A   D E
Ooh,___ ooh, ooh.   Ooh,___ ooh, ooh.

(E)   A/C# D   A   E
And if you were to ask me after all that we've been through

        A/C# D   A E
Still be - lieve in magic, oh yes I do.

     A/C# D A   E
Oh, yes I do, yes I do.

     A/C# D   A   E
Oh, yes I do, of course I do.

Outro   ‖: D | D A | E | E A/C# :‖ *Repeat to fade*

Messed Up Kids

Words & Music by Jake Bugg, Iain Archer & Brendan Benson

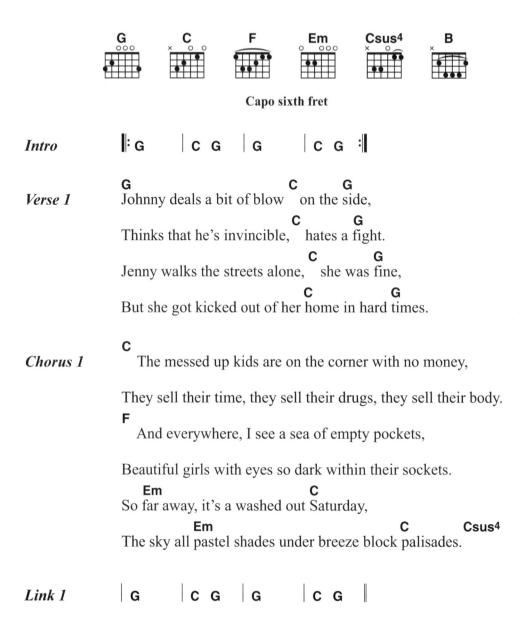

Capo sixth fret

Intro ‖: G │ C G │ G │ C G :‖

Verse 1
    G   C   G
Johnny deals a bit of blow   on the side,
                          C   G
Thinks that he's invincible,   hates a fight.
                        C   G
Jenny walks the streets alone,   she was fine,
                        C   G
But she got kicked out of her home in hard times.

Chorus 1
C
   The messed up kids are on the corner with no money,

They sell their time, they sell their drugs, they sell their body.
F
   And everywhere, I see a sea of empty pockets,

Beautiful girls with eyes so dark within their sockets.
   Em   C
So far away, it's a washed out Saturday,
          Em   C   Csus4
The sky all pastel shades under breeze block palisades.

Link 1 │ G │ C G │ G │ C G ‖

Verse 2

    G   C   G
Lights are smashed the streets are closed   in the town,

                              C   G
Places no one really goes to hang a - round.

                         C   G
Gave up on us long ago with no hope,

                                C   G
All you hear's the cold wind blow   and get stoned.

Chorus 2

    C
    The messed up kids are on the corner with no money,

They sell their time, they sell their drugs, they sell their body.

    F
    And everywhere, I see a sea of empty pockets,

Beautiful girls with eyes so dark within their sockets.

      Em   C
So far away, it's a washed out Saturday,

           Em   B
The sky all pastel shades under breeze block palisades.

Instrumental ‖: G | C G | G | C G :‖

Chorus 3   As Chorus 2

Outro | G | C G | G | C G |

                | G | C G | G | C G ‖

Only Love Can Hurt Like This

Words & Music by Diane Warren

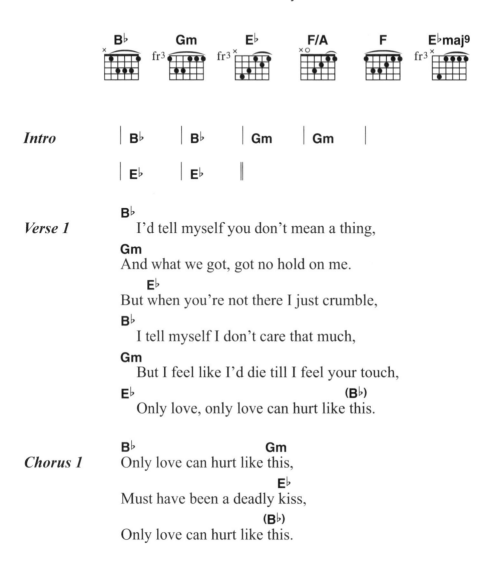

Intro | B♭ | B♭ | Gm | Gm |

| E♭ | E♭ ‖

Verse 1

B♭
   I'd tell myself you don't mean a thing,
Gm
And what we got, got no hold on me.
   E♭
But when you're not there I just crumble,
B♭
   I tell myself I don't care that much,
Gm
   But I feel like I'd die till I feel your touch,
E♭   (B♭)
   Only love, only love can hurt like this.

Chorus 1

B♭   Gm
Only love can hurt like this,
           E♭
Must have been a deadly kiss,
       (B♭)
Only love can hurt like this.

Verse 2

B♭
Say I wouldn't care if you walked away,

Gm
But every time you're there I'm begging you to stay.

E♭
When you come close I just tremble.

B♭
And every time, every time you go,

Gm
It's like a knife that cuts right to my soul,

E♭   **(B♭)**
Only love, only love can hurt like this.

Chorus 2

B♭   **Gm**
Only love can hurt like this,

                          E♭
Must have been a deadly kiss,

                          B♭
Only love can hurt like this.

                          Gm
Only love can hurt like this,

                           E♭
Your kisses burn into my skin,

                   B♭   **F/A**   **Gm**
Only love can hurt like this.

Bridge

Gm
But it's the sweetest pain,

E♭
Burning hot through my veins,

F
Love is torture makes me more sure.

N.C.   **B♭**   **Gm** **E♭**
Only love can hurt like this.

45

Chorus 3

   E♭   B♭
Only love can hurt like this,

                     Gm
Only love can hurt like this,

                       E♭
Must have been a deadly kiss.

                     B♭
Only love can hurt like this,

                     Gm
Only love can hurt like this,

                       E♭
Your kisses burn into my skin,

                   B♭   Gm
Only love can hurt like this.

Outro

   Gm   E♭maj⁹
Only love can hurt like this,

B♭
   Save me, save me,

      Gm
Only love, only love,

                        E♭
'Cause only love can hurt like this

                      N.C.(B♭)
And it must have been the deadly kiss.

Rather Be

Words & Music by James Napier, Grace Chatto & Jack Patterson

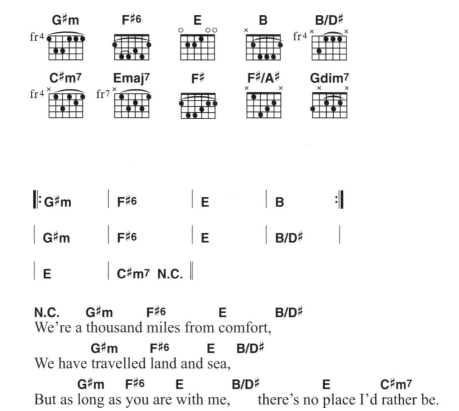

Intro

‖: G♯m | F♯6 | E | B :‖

| G♯m | F♯6 | E | B/D♯ |

| E | C♯m7 N.C. ‖

Verse 1

    N.C.   G♯m   F♯6   E   B/D♯
We're a thousand miles from comfort,

    G♯m   F♯6   E   B/D♯
We have travelled land and sea,

    G♯m F♯6   E   B/D♯   E   C♯m7
But as long as you are with me,   there's no place I'd rather be.

G♯m F♯6   E   B/D♯ G♯m F♯6 E   B/D♯
I would wait for - ever,   ex - alted in the scene,

    G♯m F♯6 E   B/D♯ E   C♯m7
As long as I am with you,   my heart con - tinues to beat.

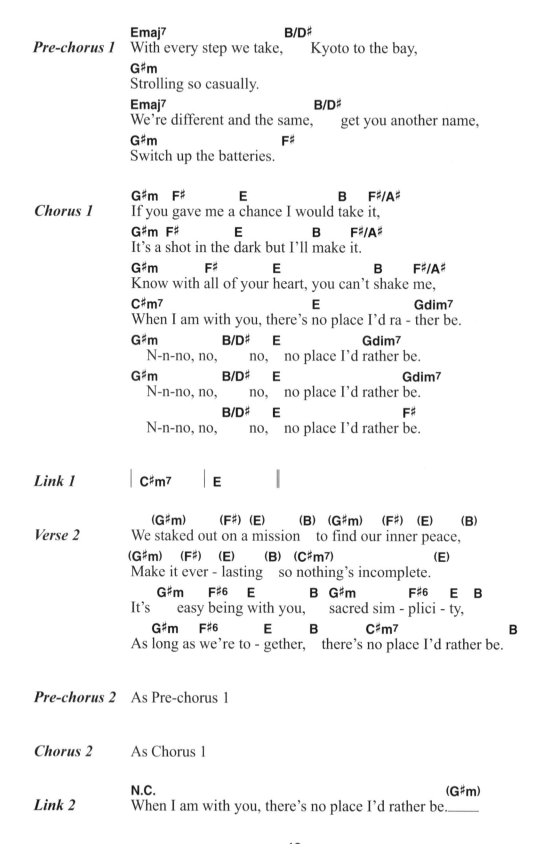

Pre-chorus 1

Emaj⁷   B/D♯
With every step we take,   Kyoto to the bay,

G♯m
Strolling so casually.

Emaj⁷   B/D♯
We're different and the same,   get you another name,

G♯m   F♯
Switch up the batteries.

Chorus 1

G♯m F♯   E   B   F♯/A♯
If you gave me a chance I would take it,

G♯m F♯   E   B   F♯/A♯
It's a shot in the dark but I'll make it.

G♯m   F♯   E   B   F♯/A♯
Know with all of your heart, you can't shake me,

C♯m⁷   E   Gdim⁷
When I am with you, there's no place I'd ra - ther be.

G♯m   B/D♯   E   Gdim⁷
  N-n-no, no,   no,   no place I'd rather be.

G♯m   B/D♯   E   Gdim⁷
  N-n-no, no,   no,   no place I'd rather be.

               B/D♯   E   F♯
  N-n-no, no,   no,   no place I'd rather be.

Link 1 | C♯m⁷ | E   ‖

Verse 2

    (G♯m)   (F♯) (E)   (B) (G♯m)   (F♯)   (E)   (B)
We staked out on a mission   to find our inner peace,

(G♯m) (F♯) (E)   (B) (C♯m⁷)   (E)
Make it ever - lasting   so nothing's incomplete.

       G♯m   F♯6   E   B G♯m   F♯6   E   B
It's   easy being with you,   sacred sim - plici - ty,

       G♯m   F♯6   E   B   C♯m⁷   B
As long as we're to - gether,   there's no place I'd rather be.

Pre-chorus 2   As Pre-chorus 1

Chorus 2   As Chorus 1

Link 2

N.C.   (G♯m)
When I am with you, there's no place I'd rather be.____

Bridge

G♯m F♯6   E   B/D♯ G♯m F♯6   E B/D♯
       Yeah. Be.____   Ooh,__ ooh.

G♯m   F♯6   E   B/D♯
Be, be, be,   be, be, be, be, be, be,

E   C♯m7   F♯
Yeah-e-yeah-e-yeah-e-yeah-e-yeah, yeah, yeah.

Chorus 3   As Chorus 1

C♯m7   Emaj7
Outro   When I am with you, there's no place I'd rather be.

Play Ball

Words & Music by Angus Young & Malcolm Young

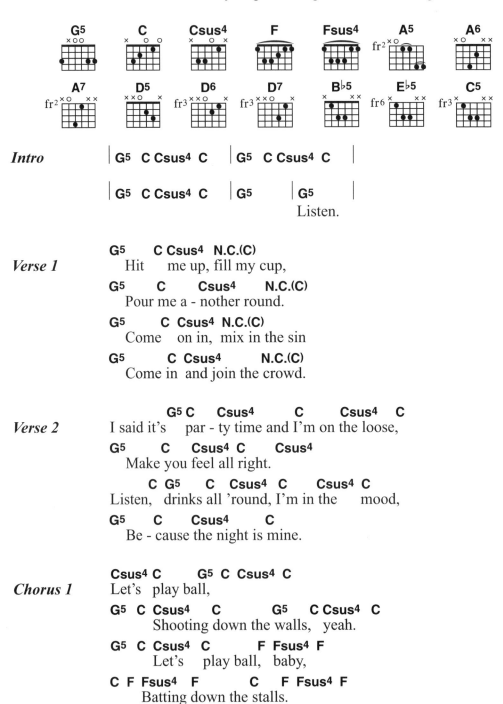

Intro

| G5 C Csus4 C | G5 C Csus4 C |

| G5 C Csus4 C | G5 | G5 |

Listen.

Verse 1

G5   C Csus4 N.C.(C)
Hit   me up, fill my cup,

G5   C   Csus4   N.C.(C)
Pour me a - nother round.

G5   C Csus4 N.C.(C)
Come   on in, mix in the sin

G5   C Csus4   N.C.(C)
Come in and join the crowd.

Verse 2

    G5 C   Csus4   C   Csus4   C
I said it's   par - ty time and I'm on the loose,

G5   C   Csus4 C   Csus4
Make you feel all right.

    C G5   C Csus4 C   Csus4 C
Listen,   drinks all 'round, I'm in the   mood,

G5   C   Csus4   C
Be - cause the night is mine.

Chorus 1

Csus4 C   G5 C Csus4 C
Let's play ball,

G5 C Csus4   C   G5   C Csus4 C
Shooting down the walls, yeah.

G5 C Csus4 C   F Fsus4 F
Let's   play ball, baby,

C F Fsus4   F   C   F Fsus4 F
Batting down the stalls.

C   F Fsus4 F   G5
Play,   play,   play ball.   Listen, Sid.

Verse 3

G⁵   C Csus⁴ C   Csus⁴ C
Light   me up, I'm in luck,

G⁵   C   Csus⁴   C Csus⁴ C
I'm un - leashed and un - bound

    G⁵ C Csus⁴ C   Csus⁴ C
Dive on   in and swim in the gin,

G⁵   C Csus⁴   C
Come on,   shout it out loud.

Chorus 2

Csus⁴ C   G⁵ C Csus⁴ C
Let's play ball,

G⁵ C Csus⁴   C   G⁵   C Csus⁴ C
    Shooting down the walls, yeah.

G⁵ C Csus⁴ C   F Fsus⁴ F
    Let's   play ball,

C F Fsus⁴ F   C   F Fsus⁴ F
    Batting down the stalls, yeah.

C   F Fsus⁴ F   G⁵
    Play,   play,   play ball.   Whoo!

Link

| A⁵ | A⁵ | A⁵ | A⁵ | |

Instrumental

| A⁵ A⁶ A⁷ | D⁵ D⁶ D⁷ D⁶ | A⁵ A⁶ A⁷ | D⁵ D⁶ D⁷ D⁶ |
                                                      Hey, yeah.

| A⁵ A⁶ A⁷ | D⁵ D⁶ D⁷ D⁶ | A⁵ A⁶ A⁷ | D⁵ D⁶ (D⁷ D⁶) |
                                That's all right now.

Chorus 3

D⁷   D⁶   G⁵ C Csus⁴ C
   Let's play ball,

G⁵ C Csus⁴   C   G⁵   C Csus⁴ C
    Shooting down the walls,   yeah.

G⁵ C Csus⁴ C   F Fsus⁴ F
    Let's   play ball,

C F Fsus⁴ F   C   F Fsus⁴ F
    Batting down the stalls,   yeah.

C F Fsus⁴ F   G⁵   Bᵇ5
    Let's play ball, let's play ball,___

           Eᵇ5 C⁵   G⁵
Let's play ball,   play, play, play ball,___ yeah.

51

Rude

Words & Music by Nasri Atweh, Adam Messinger,
Ben Spivak, Mark Pellizzer & Alexander Tanasijczuk

G♭   A♭   D♭   B♭m   D♭/F   Fm/C

Verse 1

G♭   A♭   D♭   B♭m
   Saturday morning jumped out of bed and put on my best suit.
G♭   A♭   D♭ B♭m
   Got in my car and raced like a jet all the way to you.
G♭   A♭   D♭   B♭m
   Knocked on your door with heart in my hand to ask you a question.
G♭   A♭   D♭   B♭m
   'Cause I know that you're an old-fashioned man, yeah.

Pre-chorus 1

G♭   A♭
Can I have your daughter for the rest of my life?
   D♭/F   B♭m
Say yes, say yes, 'cause I need to know.
     G♭   A♭
You say I'll never get your blessing till the day I die,
    D♭   Fm/C   B♭m
Tough luck, my friend, but the answer is no.

Chorus 1

G♭   A♭   D♭
   Why you gotta be so rude?
      B♭m
Don't you know I'm human too?
G♭   A♭   D♭
   Why you gotta be so rude?
      B♭m
I'm gonna marry her anyway.
G♭   A♭
Marry that girl, marry her anyway,
D♭   B♭m
Marry that girl, yeah, no matter what you say.
G♭   A♭
Marry that girl and we'll be a family,
D♭   B♭m   G♭   A♭ D♭ B♭m
   Why you gotta be so rude?____

Verse 2

G♭   A♭   D♭   B♭m
I hate to do this, you leave no choice, can't live without her.

G♭   A♭   D♭   B♭m
Love me or hate me, we will be both standing at that altar.

G♭   A♭   D♭   B♭m
Or we will run away   to another galaxy, you know.

G♭   A♭   D♭   B♭m
You know she's in love with me,   she will go anywhere I go.

Pre-chorus 2

G♭   A♭
Can I have your daughter for the rest of my life?

    D♭/F   B♭m
Say yes, say yes, 'cause I need to know.

        G♭   A♭
You say I'll never get your blessing till the day I die,

     D♭   Fm/C   B♭m
Tough luck, my friend, 'cause the answer's still no.

Chorus 2   As Chorus 1

Link

G♭   A♭ D♭ B♭m
Rude.____

Instrumental ‖: G♭ | A♭ | D♭ | B♭m   :‖

Pre-chorus 3

G♭   A♭
Can I have your daughter for the rest of my life?

    D♭/F   B♭m
Say yes, say yes, 'cause I need to know.

        G♭   A♭
You say, I'll never get your blessing till the day I die,

     D♭   Fm/C   B♭m
Tough luck, my friend, but no still means no.

Chorus 3

G♭   A♭   D♭
 Why you gotta be so rude?

         B♭m
Don't you know I'm human too?

G♭   A♭   D♭
 Why you gotta be so rude?

     B♭m
I'm gonna marry her anyway.

G♭   A♭
Marry that girl, marry her anyway,

D♭   B♭m
Marry that girl, yeah, no matter what you say.

G♭   A♭
Marry that girl and we'll be a family,

D♭   B♭m G♭ A♭
 Why you gotta be so rude?____

D♭   B♭m G♭ A♭
 Why you gotta be so rude?____

D♭   B♭m
 Why you gotta be so rude?

Shake It Off

Words & Music by Max Martin, Taylor Swift & Shellback

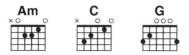

Verse 1

     N.C.   **Am**
I stay out too late,

              C
Got nothing in my brain,

              G
That's what people say, mmm-mmm.

That's what people say, mmm-mmm.

                Am
I go on too many dates,

              C
But I can't make them stay,

               G
At least that's what people say, mmm-mmm.

That's what people say, mmm-mmm.

Pre-chorus 1

     N.C.   **Am**
But I keep cruising,

               C
Can't stop, won't stop moving.

          G
It's like I got this music in my mind

Saying, "It's gonna be all right."

Chorus 1

N.C.   Am
'Cause the players gonna play, play, play, play, play,

       C
And the haters gonna hate, hate, hate, hate, hate.

      G
Baby, I'm just gonna shake, shake, shake, shake, shake,

I shake it off, I shake it off.

       Am
Heart-breakers gonna break, break, break, break, break,

       C
And the fakers gonna fake, fake, fake, fake, fake.

      G
Baby, I'm just gonna shake, shake, shake, shake, shake,

I shake it off, I shake it off.

Verse 2

N.C.   Am
I never miss a beat,

       C
I'm lightning on my feet,

       G
And that's what they don't see, mmm-mmm.

That's what they don't see, mmm-mmm.

       Am
I'm dancing on my own, (dancing on my own)

       C
I make the moves up as I go, (moves up as I go)

       G
And that's what they don't know, mmm-mmm.

That's what they don't know, mmm-mmm.

Pre-chorus 2   As Pre-chorus 1

Chorus 2   As Chorus 1

Chorus 3

N.C.
Shake it off, I shake it off,

C
I, I, I shake it off, I shake it off,

G
I, I, I shake it off, I shake it off,

I, I, I shake it off, I shake it off.

Bridge

N.C.
Hey, hey, hey.

Just think while you've been getting down and out,

About the liars and the dirty, dirty cheats of the world,

You could've been getting down to this sick beat.

My ex-man brought his new girlfriend,

She's like "Oh, my god!" but I'm just gonna shake.

And to the fella over there with the hella good hair,

Won't you come on over, baby? We can shake, shake, shake.

Yeah oh.

Chorus 4   As Chorus 1

Chorus 5

Am
‖: Shake it off, I shake it off,

C
I, I, I shake it off, I shake it off (you've got to),

G
I, I, I shake it off, I shake it off,

I, I, I shake it off, I shake it off. :‖ *Play 3 times*

Seasons (Waiting On You)

Words & Music by John Welmers, Samuel Herring & William Cashion

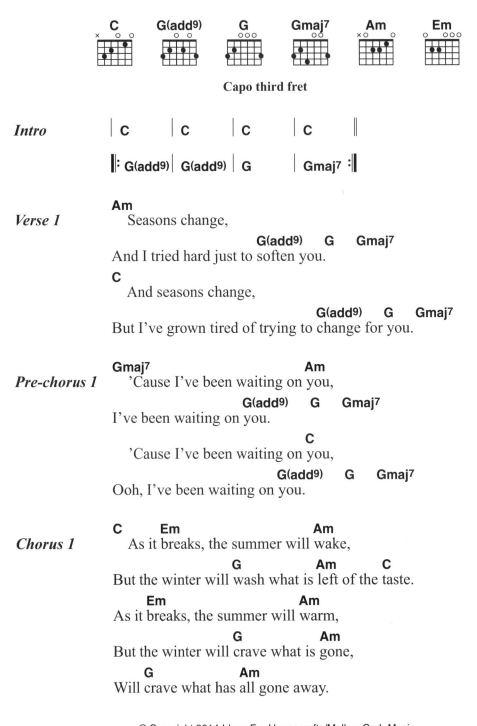

Capo third fret

Intro

| C | C | C | C ‖

‖: G(add9) | G(add9) | G | Gmaj7 :‖

Verse 1

Am
Seasons change,

        G(add9) G Gmaj7
And I tried hard just to soften you.

C
 And seasons change,

           G(add9) G Gmaj7
But I've grown tired of trying to change for you.

Pre-chorus 1

Gmaj7   **Am**
 'Cause I've been waiting on you,

     G(add9) G Gmaj7
I've been waiting on you.

          C
 'Cause I've been waiting on you,

       G(add9) G Gmaj7
Ooh, I've been waiting on you.

Chorus 1

C Em   **Am**
 As it breaks, the summer will wake,

        G   **Am**   **C**
But the winter will wash what is left of the taste.

   Em   **Am**
As it breaks, the summer will warm,

        G   **Am**
But the winter will crave what is gone,

   G   **Am**
Will crave what has all gone away.

Verse 2

Am
People change,

                                                 G(add9)   **G**   **Gmaj7**
But you know some people never do.

C
    You know when people change,

                                                 G(add9)   **G**   **Gmaj7**
They gain a peace but they lose one too.

Pre-chorus 2

Gmaj7   **Am**
'Cause I've been hanging on you,

                                           G(add9)   **G**   **Gmaj7**
Ooh, I've been waiting on you.

                                   C
'Cause I've been waiting on you,

                                           G(add9)   **G**   **Gmaj7**
Ooh, I've been hanging on you.

Chorus 2

C   **Em**   **Am**
    As it breaks, the summer will wake,

                   G   **Am**   **C**
But the winter will wash what is left of the taste.

    Em   **Am**
As it breaks, the summer will warm,

                   G   **Am**
But the winter will crave what is gone,

    G   **Am**
Will crave what is gone,

    G   **Am**
Will crave what has all gone away.

Outro

| **Am** | **Am** | **Am** | **Am** | |

| **G** | **G** | **G** | **G** | ‖

(G)   **Am**
'Cause I've been waiting on you.

She Looks So Perfect

Words & Music by Michael Clifford, Ashton Irwin & Jacob Sinclair

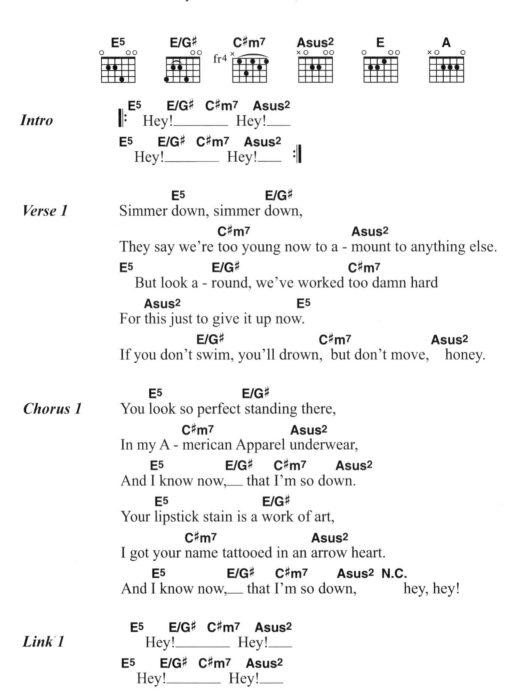

Intro

```
  E5     E/G♯  C♯m7  Asus2
‖: Hey!_____ Hey!___
  E5     E/G♯  C♯m7  Asus2
   Hey!_____ Hey!___ :‖
```

Verse 1

```
        E5              E/G♯
Simmer down, simmer down,
            C♯m7              Asus2
They say we're too young now to a - mount to anything else.
E5          E/G♯            C♯m7
 But look a - round, we've worked too damn hard
     Asus2              E5
For this just to give it up now.
          E/G♯           C♯m7         Asus2
If you don't swim, you'll drown, but don't move,   honey.
```

Chorus 1

```
        E5           E/G♯
You look so perfect standing there,
         C♯m7            Asus2
In my A - merican Apparel underwear,
    E5       E/G♯  C♯m7    Asus2
And I know now,__ that I'm so down.
        E5              E/G♯
Your lipstick stain is a work of art,
         C♯m7              Asus2
I got your name tattooed in an arrow heart.
    E5       E/G♯  C♯m7    Asus2 N.C.
And I know now,__ that I'm so down,      hey, hey!
```

Link 1

```
   E5    E/G♯  C♯m7  Asus2
   Hey!_____ Hey!___
  E5    E/G♯  C♯m7  Asus2
   Hey!_____ Hey!___
```

Verse 2

        E5   **E/G♯**
Let's get out, let's get out,
        C♯m7   **Asus2**
'Cause this dead-beat town's only here just to keep us down.
E5   **E/G♯** **C♯m7**   **Asus2**
   While I was out, I found myself a - lone just thinking,
    E5   **E/G♯**
If I showed up with a plane ticket
        C♯m7   **Asus2**
And a shiny dia-mond ring with your name on it
       E5   **E/G♯**
Would you wanna run away too?
       C♯m7   **Asus2**
'Cause all I really want is you.

Chorus 2

       E5   **E/G♯**
You look so perfect standing there,
        C♯m7   **Asus2**
In my A - merican Apparel underwear,
       E5   **E/G♯** **C♯m7**   **Asus2**
And I know now,__ that I'm so down.
         E5   **E/G♯**
I made a mixtape straight out of ninety-four,
         C♯m7   **Asus2**
I've got your ripped skinny jeans lying on the floor,
       E5   **E/G♯** **C♯m7**   **Asus2 N.C.**
And I know now,__ that I'm so down,   hey, hey!

Link 2   As Link 1

Chorus 3

       E   **E/G♯**
You look so perfect standing there,
        C♯m7   **A**
In my A - merican Apparel underwear,
       E   **E/G♯** **C♯m7**   **A**
And I know now,__ that I'm so down.
       E   **E/G♯**
Your lipstick stain is a work of art,
        C♯m7   **A**
I got your name tattooed in an arrow heart.
       E   **E/G♯** **C♯m7**   **A N.C.**
And I know now,__ that I'm so down, hey, hey!

61

Link 3   As Link 1

Chorus 4

      E5   E/G♯
You look so perfect standing there,

        C♯m7   Asus2
In my A - merican Apparel underwear,

      E5   E/G♯ C♯m7   Asus2
And I know now,— that I'm so down.

      E5   E/G♯
Your lipstick stain is a work of art,

        C♯m7   Asus2
I got your name tattooed in an arrow heart.

      E5   E/G♯ C♯m7   Asus2   E
And I know now,— that I'm so down,   hey, hey!

Sing

Words & Music by Pharrell Williams & Ed Sheeran

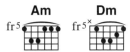

Am   Dm

To match original recording, tune guitar down a semitone

Riff reference

riff 1 ─────────────────────
E	D	C	B	A	A	A		A	A	A	G	A
2fr	5fr	3fr	2fr	5fr	5fr	5fr		5fr	5fr	5fr	3fr	5fr
④	⑤	⑤	⑤	⑥	⑥	⑥		⑥	⑥	⑥	⑥	⑥

riff 2 ─────────────────────
A	B	C	D	D	D	D		D	D	D	G	A
5fr	2fr	3fr	5fr	5fr	5fr	5fr		5fr	5fr	5fr	3fr	5fr
⑥	⑤	⑤	⑤	⑤	⑤	⑤		⑤	⑤	⑤	⑥	⑥

Intro | Am | Am | Am | Am ‖

Verse 1

       N.C.   **Am (riff 1)**
It's late in the eve - ning, glass on the side,

             riff 1
I've been sat with you   for most of the night,

      Dm (riff 2)
Ignoring everybody here we wish they would disappear

       riff 2
So maybe we could get down now.

Am (riff 1)   **riff 1**
I don't wanna know if you're getting ahead of the pro - gram,

           Dm (riff 2)
I want you to be mine, lady, and to hold your body close.

         riff 2
Take another step into the no-man's land

For the longest time, lady.

Pre-chorus 1

    Am
I need you darling, come on set the tone,

If you feel you're falling, won't you let me know?

     Dm
Oh, oh-oh-oh, ooh-ooh, oh, oh-oh-oh, ooh-ooh.

cont.

Am
If you love me come on get involved,

Feel it rushing through you from your head to toe.
Dm
Oh, oh-oh-oh, ooh-ooh, oh, oh-oh-oh, ooh-ooh. Sing!

Pre-chorus 1

Am (riff 1)
Oh, oh, oh, oh-oh, oh, oh, oh, oh, oh, oh, oh-oh.
riff 1
Oh, oh, oh, oh-oh, oh, oh, oh, oh, oh, oh, oh-oh. Louder!
Dm (riff 2)
Oh, oh, oh, oh-oh, oh, oh, oh, oh, oh, oh, oh-oh. Sing!
riff 2
Oh, oh, oh, oh-oh, oh, oh, oh, oh, oh, oh, oh-oh.

Rap

N.C.   **Am (riff 1)**
This love is a - blaze, I saw flames from the side of the stage

And the fire brigade comes in a couple of days.
　　　riff 1
Until then we got nothing to say and nothing to know,

But something to drink and maybe something to smoke.
Dm (riff 2)
　Let it go until our roads are changed,

Singing "We Found Love" in a local rave, no,
riff 2
I don't really know what I'm supposed to say

But I can just figure it out and hope and pray.
　Am (riff 1)
I told her my name and said, "It's nice to meet ya."

Then she handed me a bottle of water filled with tequila.
riff 1
I already know she's a keeper,

Just from this one small act of kindness
　　Dm (riff 2)
I'm in deep, deep. If anybody finds out,

I'm meant to drive home but I've drunk all of it now.
　　riff 2
Not sobering up we just sit on the couch,

One thing led to another, now she's kissing my mouth.

64

Pre-chorus 2   As Pre-chorus 1

Chorus 2   As Chorus 1

                     Am
Bridge   Can you feel it?

                All the guys in here don't even wanna dance.

                Can you feel it?

                All that I can hear is music from the back.
                     Dm
                Can you feel it?

                Found you hiding here so won't you take my hand darling

                Before the beat kicks in again?
                     Am
                Can you feel it? Ooh, ah, oh.
                     Dm
                Can you feel it? Ooh, no, no, no, whoa, no, no.

                N.C.   Am (riff 1)
Chorus 3   Sing! I need you darling, come on set the tone,
                     riff 1
                If you feel you're falling, won't you let me know?
                          Dm (riff 2)
                Oh, oh-oh-oh, ooh-ooh.
                          riff 2
                Oh, oh-oh-oh, ooh-ooh. Sing!
                Am (riff 1)
                If you love me come on get involved,
                     riff 1
                Feel it rushing through you from your head to toe.
                          Dm (riff 2)
                Oh, oh-oh-oh, ooh-ooh.
                          riff 2
                Oh, oh-oh-oh, ooh-ooh. Sing!

Stay With Me

Words & Music by Tom Petty, Jeff Lynne,
James Napier, Sam Smith & William Phillips

Intro | Am⁷ F | C | Am⁷ F | C   ‖

Verse 1

Am⁷   F   C
   Guess it's true, I'm not good at a one night stand,
Am⁷   F   C
   But I still need love 'cause I'm just a man.
Am⁷   F   C
   These nights never seem to go to plan,
Am⁷   F/G   C
   I don't want you to leave, will you hold my hand?

Chorus 1

(C)   Am⁷   F   C
Oh, won't you   stay___ with me?
                 Am⁷ F C
   'Cause you're   all___ I need.
G   Am⁷   F   C
This ain't love, it's   clear to see,
        E⁷/G♯ Am⁷   F   C
But darling,   stay   with me.

Verse 2

Am⁷   F   C
   Why am I so emo - tional?
Am⁷   F   C
   No, it's not a good look, gain some self-control.
Am⁷   F   C
   And deep down I know this ne - ver works,
Am⁷   F/G   C
   But you can lay with me so it does - n't hurt.

Chorus 2   As Chorus 1

Instrumental | **Am7 F** | **C** | **Am7 F** | **C** |

                        | **Am7 F** | **C** | **Am7 F/G** | **C**   ‖

Chorus 3   As Chorus 1

Chorus 4   As Chorus 1

Steal My Girl

Words & Music by Wayne Hector, John Ryan, Julian Bunetta, Ed Drewett, Liam Payne & Louis Tomlinson

Asus4   A   Asus2   D   Dmaj7   D6   E

Capo first fret
(tune guitar slightly sharp)

Intro   ‖: Asus4 A | Asus2 A | Asus4 A | Asus2 A |

| D Dmaj7 | D6 Dmaj7 | D Dmaj7 | D6 Dmaj7 :‖

Verse 1

A
She been my queen since we were sixteen,

We want the same things, we dream the same dreams, all right.
D Dmaj7 D6 Dmaj7   D Dmaj7 D6 Dmaj7
                       All right.

A
I got it all 'cause she is the one,

Her mom calls me love, her dad calls me son, all right.
D Dmaj7 D6 Dmaj7   D Dmaj7 D6 Dmaj7
                       All right.

Pre-chorus 1
E   D
I know, I know, I know for sure.

Chorus 1
Asus4   A   Asus4   A
Every - body wanna steal my girl,
Asus4   A   Asus4   A
Every - body wanna take her heart away.
D   Dmaj7   D6   Dmaj7
Couple billion in the whole wide world,
D   Dmaj7   D6   Dmaj7
Find an - other one 'cause she be - longs to me.

cont.

Asus⁴   **A**   **Asus⁴**   **A**
Every - body wanna steal my girl,

Asus⁴   **A**   **Asus⁴**   **A**
Every - body wanna take her heart away.

D   **Dmaj⁷**   **D⁶**   **Dmaj⁷**
Couple billion in the whole wide world,

D   **Dmaj⁷**   **D⁶**   **Dmaj⁷**
Find an - other one 'cause she be - longs to me.

Chorus 2

Asus⁴ A   Asus⁴ A
Na, na, na,   na, na-na.

Asus⁴ A   Asus⁴ A
Na, na, na,   na, na-na.

D   Dmaj⁷ D⁶ Dmaj⁷
Na, na,   na, na, na-na.

D   Dmaj⁷ D⁶   Dmaj⁷
Na, na,   she be - longs to me.

Verse 2

A
Kisses like cream, her walk is so mean

And every jaw drop when she's in those jeans, all right.
D Dmaj⁷ D⁶ Dmaj⁷   D Dmaj⁷ D⁶ Dmaj⁷
All right.

A
I don't exist if I don't have her,

The sun doesn't shine, the world doesn't turn, all right.
D Dmaj⁷ D⁶ Dmaj⁷   D Dmaj⁷ D⁶ Dmaj⁷
All right.

Pre-chorus 2   As Pre-chorus 1

Chorus 3   As Chorus 1

Chorus 4

Asus⁴ A Asus⁴ A
  Na, na, na,   na, na-na.

Asus⁴ A Asus⁴ A
  Na, na, na,   na, na-na.

D   Dmaj⁷ D⁶ Dmaj⁷
  Na, na,   na, na, na-na.

D   Dmaj⁷ D⁶ Dmaj⁷
  Na, na,   na, na, na-na.

Bridge

     E
She knows, she knows

        D
That I've never let her down before.

     E
She knows, she knows

        D
That I'm never gonna let another take her love from me now.

Chorus 5   As Chorus 1

Chorus 6   As Chorus 4

Chorus 7

Asus⁴ A Asus⁴ A
  Na, na, na,   na, na-na.

Asus⁴ A Asus⁴ A
  Na, na, na,   na, na-na.

D   Dmaj⁷ D⁶ Dmaj⁷
  Na, na,   na, na, na-na.

D Dmaj⁷ D⁶   Dmaj⁷ N.C.
    She be-longs to me.

Superheroes

Words & Music by Mark Sheehan, Daniel O'Donoghue & James Barry

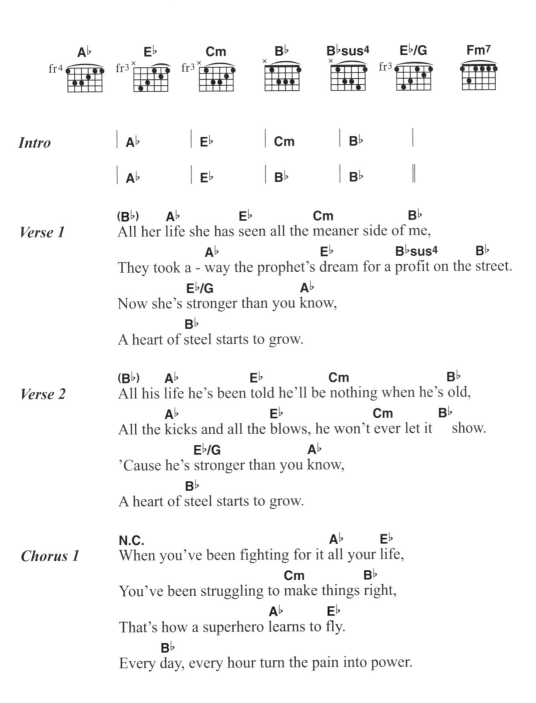

Intro

| A♭ | E♭ | Cm | B♭ | |

| A♭ | E♭ | B♭ | B♭ | ‖

Verse 1

(B♭) A♭   E♭   Cm   B♭
All her life she has seen all the meaner side of me,
             A♭   E♭   B♭sus4   B♭
They took a - way the prophet's dream for a profit on the street.
       E♭/G   A♭
Now she's stronger than you know,
      B♭
A heart of steel starts to grow.

Verse 2

(B♭) A♭   E♭   Cm   B♭
All his life he's been told he'll be nothing when he's old,
    A♭   E♭   Cm   B♭
All the kicks and all the blows, he won't ever let it   show.
       E♭/G   A♭
'Cause he's stronger than you know,
      B♭
A heart of steel starts to grow.

Chorus 1

N.C.   A♭   E♭
When you've been fighting for it all your life,
             Cm   B♭
You've been struggling to make things right,
         A♭   E♭
That's how a superhero learns to fly.
    B♭
Every day, every hour turn the pain into power.

cont.

                                               A♭   **E♭**
(When you've been fighting) for it all your life,

                         Cm   **B♭**
You've been working every day and night,

                 A♭   **E♭**
That's how a superhero learns to fly.

       B♭
Every day, every hour turn the pain into power.

Link

A♭   **E♭ Cm**   **B♭**
Oh, oh - oh, oh, oh, oh - oh.

Verse 3

(B♭)   **A♭**   **E♭**   **Cm**   **B♭**
All the hurt, all the lies, all the tears that they cry,

         A♭   **E♭**   **Cm**   **B♭**
When the moment is just right you see fire in their eyes.

          E♭/G   **A♭**
'Cause he's stronger than you know,

       B♭
A heart of steel starts to grow.

Chorus 2   As Chorus 1

Instrumental | **A♭** | **E♭** | **Cm** | **B♭** |

                | **A♭** | **E♭** |

               B♭
Every day, every hour turn the pain into power.

                | **A♭** | **E♭** | **Cm** | **B♭** |

                | **A♭** | **E♭** |

               B♭
Every day, every hour turn the pain into power.

Bridge

(B♭)   **A♭**   **E♭**
She's got lions in her heart   and a fire in her soul,

        Cm   **B♭**
He's a got a beast in his belly that's so hard to control.

         A♭   **E♭**
'Cause they've taken too much hits, taking blow by blow,

      B♭sus4   **B♭**
Now light a match, stand back, watch them explode.

        Fm7   **A♭**
She's got lions in her heart and a fire in her soul,

        E♭   **B♭**
He's a got a beast in his belly that's so hard to control.

        E♭/G   **A♭**
'Cause they've taken too much hits, taking blow by blow,

      B♭sus4   **B♭**
Now light a match, stand back, watch them explode.

Chorus 3   As Chorus 1

Chorus 4 | **A♭** | **E♭** | **Cm** | **B♭** |

      A♭   **E♭**
Oh, yeah.

      B♭
Every day, every hour turn the pain into power.

A♭ **E♭**   **Cm** **B♭**   **A♭** **E♭**
    Ooh, yeah,   whoa.

      B♭
Every day, every hour turn the pain into power.

                           A♭   **E♭**
(When you've been fighting) for it all your life,

                   Cm   **B♭**
You've been struggling to make things right,

                A♭   **E♭** **B♭**
That's how a superhero learns to fly.____

73

Take Me To Church

Words & Music by Andrew Hozier-Byrne

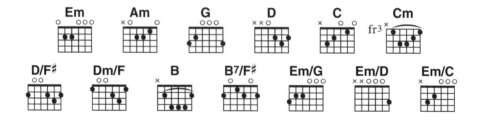

Verse 1

  Em   Am Em   Am
  My lover's got humour, she's the giggle at a funeral.

 G   Am Em
  Knows everybody's disap - proval,

           Am
I should've worshipped her sooner.

 Em   Am   Em   Am
  If the heavens ever did speak, she's the last true mouthpiece.

 G   Am   Em   Am
  Every Sunday's getting more bleak, a fresh poison each week.

 D   C
  We were born sick, you heard them say it,

 Em   Am Em
  My church offers no abso - lutes.

            Am
She tells me, worship in the bedroom.

 G   Am Em   Am
  The only heaven I'll be sent to is when I'm alone with you.

 D   C
  I was born sick, but I love it, command me to be well.

   G C G   C G   Cm G
  A - A - men. A - men. A - men.

G D/F♯   Dm/F Em   B
     Take me to church, I'll worship like a dog at the shrine of your lies,

                                      G
I'll tell you my sins and you can sharpen your knife.

               Am
Offer me that deathless death,

      Em   Am G
Good God, let me give you my life.

        D/F♯ Em   B
Take me to church, I'll worship like a dog at the shrine of your lies,

                                        G
I'll tell you my sins and you can sharpen your knife.

               Am
Offer me that deathless death,

      Em   Am G D/F♯
Good God, let me give you my life.

Verse 2

Em   Am   Em   Am
  If I'm a pagan of the good times,   my lover's the sunlight.

G   Am   Em   Am
  To keep the goddess on my side,   she demands a sac - rifice.

D   C
  Drain the whole sea,   get something shiny.

Em   Am   Em
  Something meaty for the main course,

                  Am
That's a fine looking high horse.

G   Am   Em   Am
  What you got in the stable?   We've a lot of starving faithful.

D   C
  That looks tasty,   that looks plenty,

This is hungry work.

Chorus 2   As Chorus 1

Bridge

C   G   B7/F♯   Em/G   Em
No masters   or kings when the ritual be - gins,

         C   G   B7/F♯   Em/G   Em
There is no sweeter innocence than our gentle sin.

         C   G   B7/F♯   Em/G   Em
In the madness and soil of that____ sad earthly scene,

         C   G   B7/F♯   Em
Only then I am human, only then I am clean.

Em/D Em/C C   G   C G   Cm G   Cm G
Oh,_____   oh,___ A - men. A - men. A - men.

Chorus 3

G D/F♯   Dm/F Em   B
Take me to church, I'll worship like a dog at the shrine of your lies

                                  G
I'll tell you my sins and you can sharpen your knife.

               Am
Offer me that deathless death,

       Em   Am G
Good God, let me give you my life.

       D/F♯ Em   B
Take me to church, I'll worship like a dog at the shrine of your lies,

                                  G
I'll tell you my sins and you can sharpen your knife.

               Am
Offer me that deathless death,

       Em   Am G D/F♯ Em
Good God, let me give you my life.

Wake Me Up

Words & Music by Aloe Blacc, Tim Bergling & Michael Einziger

Am   F   C   Gsus4   G   E

Capo second fret

Intro | Am | F | C | Gsus4 G |

| Am | F | C | G   E ‖

Verse 1

Am   F   C
   Feeling my way through the darkness,

Am   F   C
   Guided by a beating heart.

Am   F   C
   I can't tell where the journey will end,

Am   F   C
   But I know where to start.

Am   F   C
   They tell me I'm too young to understand,

Am   F   C
   They say I'm caught up in a dream.

Am   F   C
   Well, life will pass me by if I don't open up my eyes,

Am   F   C
   Well, that's fine by me.

Chorus 1

(C)   Am   F   C
So wake me up when it's all over,

G   Am   F   C
When I'm wiser and I'm older.

E   Am   F   C
All this time I was finding my - self

         G Am   F   C
And I___   didn't know I was lost.

     E   Am   F   C
So wake me up when it's all over,

G   Am   F   C
When I'm wiser and I'm older.

E   Am   F   C
All this time I was finding my - self

         G Am   F   C
And I___   didn't know I was lost.

Link

‖: Am | F | C | C   G |

| Am | F | C | C   E |

| Am | F | C | C   G |

| Am | F | D | C   E :‖ *Play 3 times*

Verse 2

Am   F   C
  I tried carrying the weight of the world,

Am   F   C
  But I only have two hands.

Am   F   C
  Hope I get the chance to travel the world,

Am   F   C
  But I don't have any plans.

Am   F   C
  Wish that I could stay for - ever this young,

Am   F   C
  Not a - fraid to close my eyes.

Am   F   C
  Life's a game made for everyone

Am   G   C
  And love is the prize.

Chorus 2

(C)   **Am**   **F**   **C**
So wake me up when it's all over,

G   **Am** **F**   **C**
When I'm wiser and I'm older.

E   **Am**   **F**   **C**
All this time I was finding my - self

        G Am   **F**   **C**
And I___   didn't know I was lost.

N.C.   **Am**   **F**   **C**
So wake me up when it's all over,

G   **Am** **F**   **C**
When I'm wiser and I'm older.

E   **Am**   **F**   **C**
All this time I was finding my - self

        G Am   **F**   **C**
And I___   didn't know I was lost.

E Am   **F**   **C**
      I didn't know I was lost.

G Am   **F**   **C**
      I didn't know I was lost.

E Am   **F**   **C**
      I didn't know I was lost.

G Am   **F**   **C**
      I didn't know.

Outro

‖: **Am** | **F** | **C** | **C** **G** |

| **Am** | **F** | **C** | **C** **E** |

| **Am** | **F** | **C** | **C** **G** |

| **Am** | **F** | **C** | **C** **E** :‖ *Play 3 times*

| **Am**   ‖

1 2 3 4 5 6 7 8 9